See the Great American E

Michael Zeiler

GreatAmericanEclipse.com

A Great American Eclipse® Publication

The splendor of totality

This photograph by Denise Kramer (eclipse-chasers.com) shows the very end of totality. This sight is called the Diamond Ring. No photograph can fully capture the beauty your eyes will see.

You cannot completely prepare yourself for the sight of a total solar eclipse. When totality arrives, you may experience primal emotions and wonderment at the unspeakable beauty of the corona and the panoply of colors and light as you've never seen before. You might cheer, gasp, or perhaps cry at this astounding vision.

You are looking straight down a billiard shot of the Earth, Moon, and Sun lined up perfectly. The fact that the Sun's and Moon's disks appear to be nearly the same apparent size allows us to see the Sun's outer atmosphere, its corona. The beauty of the corona is hidden from us all our lives except for the very special moments during totality.

When you look at the total eclipse, you will see the blackest black imaginable where the Moon is, surrounded by the Sun's ever-changing outer atmosphere, the corona. The quality of light is stupendous with an amazing light show of iridescence, scintillation, and delicate colors.

Another thought that may strike you during totality is that you are watching the solar system in motion. In real-time, you can experience the orbital motions of the Moon around the Earth and the Earth around the Sun.

Even for those who have seen it before, a total solar eclipse is an intensely emotional experience. You may feel ecstasy, wonder, and regret when it is over. If totality touches you like it does many others, you will immediately make plans to see the next one.

The background photo shows the sky's appearance during totality. Planets and brighter stars are visible and you will see darkening rotating over the horizon as the Moon's shadow passes.

See the Great American Eclipse of August 21, 2017

Included — Two solar eclipse viewing glasses!

Everything you need to know about the eclipse plus detailed maps of the best places to go

Michael Zeiler
GreatAmericanEclipse.com

Have you ever seen a total solar eclipse?

Many people have seen a partial solar eclipse when the Moon covers only a part of the Sun. You may have seen the eclipsed Sun in pinhole projections or the fascinating display of tiny eclipsed Sun figures in shadows cast by tree leaves. While partial solar eclipses are interesting, daylight is mostly unchanged and you might not even know that an eclipse is happening without having heard about it.

But few people have seen the astonishing sight of a total solar eclipse when day turns to a deep twilight and the Sun's magnificent corona shimmers in the darkened sky. Total solar eclipses are rarely seen because the path of total eclipse is narrow and only visits a spot on Earth once every 375 years or so on average.

On August 21, 2017, a total solar eclipse visits the United States and it's called the Great American Eclipse because it will be so accessible to hundreds of millions of Americans. Remarkably, this will be the very first total solar eclipse to pass over the United States exclusively, since the country's founding in 1776!

The path of totality bisects the nation from Oregon to South Carolina and nearly all Americans can reach the path of totality within a day's drive. You can plan a summer vacation around the eclipse and there will be many camping areas along the path especially set up to accommodate all who show up.

This book is your guide to nature's grandest sight and provides practical advice, background information, and detailed maps to enhance your odds of seeing this spectacular event. The breathtaking sight of the total solar eclipse will be the memory of a lifetime!

The exquisite image of the solar corona on the cover is courtesy of Miloslav Druckmüller, whose work can be found at http://www.zam.fme.vutbr.cz/~druck/Eclipse. All maps in this book are the original work of the author, Michael Zeiler, and most of these maps use eclipse computations by Xavier Jubier, xjubier.free.fr, and eclipse predictions by Fred Espenak, eclipsewise.com. The maps in this book are created using ArcGIS software by Esri (esri.com). Unless otherwise credited, images in this book are by the author or in the public domain.

How to safely view the eclipse

Whether you are inside or outside the path of the total solar eclipse, you will need a safe viewing method to view the eclipse while any part of the Sun is still visible.

From the first nibble of the Moon inside the Sun to the end, the eclipse will last about 2 to 3 hours depending on location. If you are inside the path of totality, you'll get about 2 minutes of totality in the middle of the partial eclipse.

Here are a few rules for eclipse viewing:

1. During the partial phase of eclipse, you must use eclipse viewing glasses certified by the International Standards Organization (ISO). You can instead use a pinhole projection method, but the view through eclipse glasses will be more satisfying.

2. Do not use any other method such as stacking sunglasses, exposed film, or CDs. Your vision is far too precious to jeopardize with substandard protection.

3. Even if you have ISO-certified eclipse viewing glasses or filters, do not use them with binoculars or telescopes. Concentrating sunlight instantly makes solar filters unsafe!

There are solar filters designed for the front end of cameras, binoculars, and telescopes, but they must be used correctly and with great care.

Once the two minutes or so of totality begins, it is safe to look directly at the totally eclipsed Sun. You will know when this moment arrives because the sky is suddenly in deep twilight. When the first bit of direct sunlight returns after two minutes or so of totality, immediately turn your eyes away from the eclipse and put on your eclipse glasses again.

While it is important to protect your vision, do not make the mistake of keeping your eclipse glasses on once the total solar eclipse begins. This is the most beautiful sight you can see in the sky and you won't want to miss it!

You can buy ISO-certified eclipse viewing glasses and filters at GreatAmericanEclipse.com and EclipseGlasses2017.com.

Sun, Moon, Earth

Total solar eclipses occur because of a remarkable cosmic coincidence: the Sun appears to be about the same size in our sky as the Moon. While the Sun is actually about 400 times larger in diameter than the Moon, it is also about 400 times farther away from us than the Moon.

This single fact explains why we see total solar eclipses — the Moon has an apparent size that just barely covers the Sun completely, yet is not too large that the Sun's outer atmosphere, its corona, is eclipsed as well. We on Earth occupy a celestial sweet spot to witness this sight.

If there are intelligent beings in other planetary systems, the odds must be quite low that they would enjoy the same circumstance as we do on Earth. So we are the beneficiaries of wonderful cosmic luck.

It was not always so. When the Moon formed around Earth over 4 billion years ago, it was much closer to Earth and appeared much larger in our sky. So total solar eclipses in the early epochs of our Earth not only blocked the Sun, but most of the corona as well.

Over the eons, the Moon has been gradually receding from Earth due to friction from tides. At present, the distance from the Earth to the Moon increases by about an inch per year. Hundreds of millions of years from now, the Moon's disk will become smaller such that no more total solar eclipses will be visible from Earth.

The background image is a composite of the Hubble deep space fields and Moon-Earth image from the NASA DISCOVR spacecraft overlaid with eclipse shadow cone and path of total solar eclipse.

Types of solar eclipses

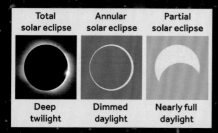

Total solar eclipse	Annular solar eclipse	Partial solar eclipse
Deep twilight	Dimmed daylight	Nearly full daylight

There are three types of solar eclipses; total, annular, and partial.

While the Moon and Sun have nearly the same apparent size in the sky, their apparent sizes slightly vary because of two factors: the Moon is in a slightly elliptical orbit around Earth and Earth also revolves in a slightly elliptical orbit around the Sun.

Because of these elliptical orbits, the Moon's disk does not completely cover the Sun's disk during an annular eclipse. These are annular solar eclipses, often called the "ring of fire." An example of this eclipse type occurred in the United States on May 20, 2012. The next annular solar eclipse that visits the United States will be on October 14, 2023.

An annular eclipse is a striking sight, but it does not command the same overwhelming sense of wonder that a total solar eclipse does. Daytime is dimmer but not twilight. Because some of the Sun's disk is still visible, it is much too bright for the Sun's corona to become visible. It's never safe to look directly at an annular solar eclipse, even at its maximum, unless you are using an ISO-certified solar filter.

If the Moon's shadow is not centered on the Earth, then another type of solar eclipse occurs, a partial solar eclipse. During a partial solar eclipse, the center of the Moon's shadow misses the Earth and from everywhere the eclipse is visible, you will only see part of the Sun eclipsed. Again, at no time during a partial solar eclipse should you look directly at the Sun without an approved solar filter or a pinhole projection.

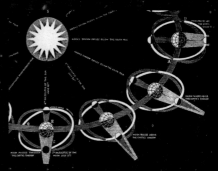

This woodcut from Smith's Illustrated Astronomy (1855) shows the inclination of the Moon's orbit relative to the Earth's orbit around the Sun.

Why doesn't a solar eclipse occur every month? If the orbit of the Moon were exactly within the same plane as the orbit of the Earth around the Sun, then some type of solar eclipse would occur every New Moon. However, the orbit of the Moon is tilted about 5 degrees with respect to the Earth's orbit around the Sun.

The partial stage of the solar eclipse lasts between two and three hours. The total phase of the solar eclipse (in the yellow band) lasts up to 2 minutes, 41 seconds.

These three maps show the times when the partial phase of the eclipse begins, ends, and the local maximum eclipse. The beginning of eclipse is when the Moon first contacts the Sun's disk and the end of the eclipse is when the Moon last touches the Sun's disk.

The white curves in each map show the progress of the eclipse for every minute and times are shown every five minutes. To determine the times for your location when the partial eclipse begins, the moment of maximum eclipse, and when the partial eclipse ends, follow the curves and be sure to adjust for any changes in time zone.

The detailed maps that start on page 22 give you precise durations of the total solar eclipse.

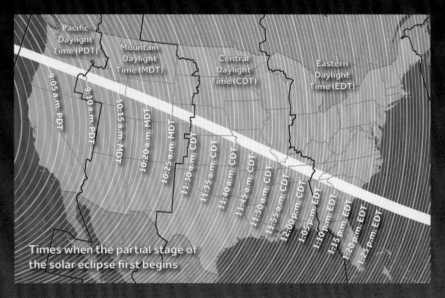

Times when the partial stage of the solar eclipse first begins

During the partial stage of the solar eclipse, you will not notice any obvious dimming of sunshine until about 75% of the Sun's diameter is eclipsed by the Moon. If you are inside the path of the total solar eclipse, this is about 15 minutes before the total solar eclipse.

During the last 15 minutes before totality, watch your environment for changes that will accelerate, especially in the last few minutes. You will start to notice shadows becoming crisper and an eerie appearance in the landscape. Watch the shadows of trees to see a projection of the eclipse. See if you can feel the temperature dropping during the eclipse.

You might see unusual behavior of birds or other animals in your environment confused by the sudden changes in light. This has been reported at many total solar eclipses.

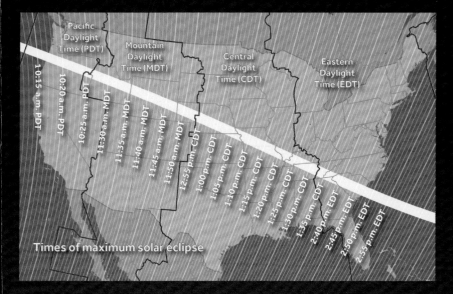

Times of maximum solar eclipse

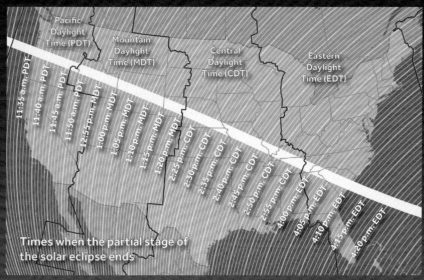

**Times when the partial stage of
the solar eclipse ends**

Watch for these phenomena before the onset of totality:

· 5-10 minutes before, Venus will become visible in the sky near the Sun

· 2-3 minutes before, the western sky will darken and shadows become very crisp

· 1 minute before, look for wavy patterns on the ground called 'shadow bands'

· In the last few seconds, the thin crescent of the Sun will rapidly disintegrate into a set of broken and brilliant bits of sunshine called the 'Baily's Beads'

· Totality begins with the display of the 'diamond ring', the last bit of sunshine silhouetted against the Sun's corona. The sky is instantly in deep twilight and a few planets and bright stars will be visible. Totality ends after about two minutes with another 'diamond ring'.

The foremost consideration for success on eclipse day is the weather. You could be in a location billed as 'the best spot to see the eclipse' but if clouds intervene, you will be profoundly disappointed when you hear the experiences of others who were luckier.

The best strategy to ensure that you see nature's grandest sight is to be informed and stay mobile.

If you have the freedom to travel throughout the nation, then you should head west. As the map of average August afternoon cloud statistics shows, the clearest skies are typically found from Oregon through Nebraska. Keep in mind that the mountainous areas of

Idaho and Wyoming may also be challenging because of thunder storms which may build over them.

Dedicated eclipse chasers will start studying weather forecasts starting about five days before the eclipse. They will head for a favorable zone and refine their location using forecasts issued shortly before the eclipse.

Should errant clouds appear on eclipse day, you should have detailed maps to quickly relocate in the last hours if needed. You can find print maps (which is important where there is no cell signal) at GreatAmericanEclipse.com/Store and a dedicated smart phone app at GreatAmericanEclipse.com/App

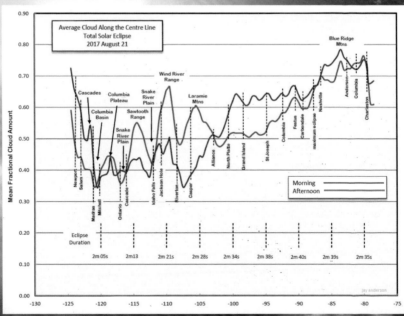

This chart by Jay Anderson, Eclipsophile.com, shows the morning and afternoon cloud statistics along the path of total solar eclipse.

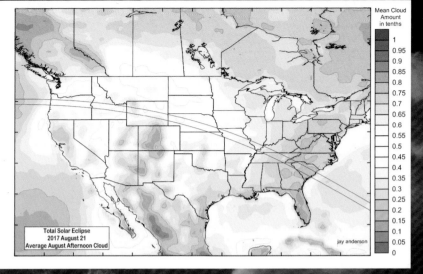

Total Solar Eclipse
2017 August 21
Average August Afternoon Cloud

jay anderson

Mean Cloud
Amount
in tenths

1
0.95
0.9
0.85
0.8
0.75
0.7
0.65
0.6
0.55
0.5
0.45
0.4
0.35
0.3
0.25
0.2
0.15
0.1
0.05
0

This map of mean cloud statistics for August afternoons shows a clear pattern of clearer skies in the western half of the United States and increased cloudiness in the eastern half of the nation.

The essential reference for eclipse climatology is Eclipsophile.com by Jay Anderson and Jennifer West. Consult this website for long-range planning as well as short term eclipse weather forecasts.

An optimal plan is to roam the western half of the nation with a recreational vehicle or tent and identify (and perhaps reserve) two or three camping locations for the eve of the eclipse to widen your range of motion up to hundreds of miles.

Some towns along the path are planning to establish temporary camping grounds for the expected heavy visitation during eclipse week. For a directory of these open camping locations, visit GreatAmericanEclipse.com in the weeks before August 2017.

These steps may seem extreme to some but with this strategy, you can substantially increase your odds of success on eclipse day.

Even if you don't have the range of movement of dedicated eclipse chasers, you can still stack your odds for success by employing strategies to stay mobile.

If you stay in a hotel or a friend or relative's home and if the weather forecast the evening before eclipse day is not favorable, leave in the pre-dawn hours towards the direction most favorable. Be sure to keep your car tank topped with fuel. An pre-dawn start will also minimize any traffic issues you may encounter.

To help you locate your optimal site on eclipse day, download the dedicated smart phone app at GreatAmericanEclipse.com/App

Great places to view the eclipse

The most frequently asked question about the eclipse is, where is the best place to view it? The truth is that there are many great places to see the eclipse and here are ten great spots to see the eclipse, weather permitting.

Sandhills of western Nebraska
Duration of totality is 2 min 30 sec
Totality beings at 11:49 a.m. MDT

The Sandhills country of Nebraska is a prime location for viewing the eclipse. A careful weather observer has taken notes over 20 years and reports that 70% of late August days are favorable for eclipse viewing. North Platte is a good staging area with hotels and good highways for distance traveling. A bonus is that you can enjoy dark summer nights and a glorious view of the Milky Way.

Madras, Oregon
Duration of totality is 2 min 4 sec
Totality begins at 10:19 a.m. PDT

While the Oregon coast is at risk of marine clouds, the interior of this state actually enjoys the nation's best weather prospects. Madras is easily accessible from Portland with a two-hour drive and sits at the junction of four highways for good mobility. A bonus is the prospect of seeing Mt. Jefferson to the west darken as totality envelops this prominent peak 17 seconds before totality in Madras.

Snake River Valley, Idaho
Duration of totality is 2 min 18 sec
Totality begins at 11:33 a.m. MDT

The Snake River Valley in eastern Idaho consists of farmland and lava fields. This area is an attractive spot for eclipse chasers because of very good weather prospects and many roads for evasive maneuvering in the event of local clouds.

Casper, Wyoming
Duration of totality is 2 min 26 sec
Totality begins at 11:42 a.m. MDT

It is for good reason that the Astronomical League is holding their annual Astrocon Conference in Casper just before eclipse day. Not only does Casper have great weather prospects, but also uncrowded highways that extend west, east, north, and south that can be used for every weather contingency.

The foremost criterion for selecting a site is the weather. Any location along the path of totality from Oregon to South Carolina can enjoy good weather on eclipse day, but the western half of the United States, especially from the Willamette Valley of Oregon to the Nebraska Sandhills, enjoys the best weather odds.

Every eclipse viewer should have a plan for mobility. Even in the sunniest locations, you don't want to be caught under a cloud during the precious two minutes of totality. Pick a location with a good highway system that you can use to relocate the day before, the morning of, or the hour before the eclipse if weather threatens. The total solar eclipse will be such a spectacle that you won't regret making the effort to find a clear viewing location.

Across the nation, the path of the total solar eclipse is between 60 and 71 miles wide. You generally want to be near the centerline of the path of totality for maximum duration of totality.

Another piece of advice is to remain flexible in your plan for eclipse day. August is a perfect time of year for camping, so consider bringing a tent or recreational vehicle in case a weather system forces you to relocate several hundred miles.

Carbondale, Illinois
Duration of totality is 2 min 41.6 sec
Totality begins at 1:20 p.m. CDT

Carbondale has a special distinction — it is near the crossing centerlines of both the August 21, 2017 total solar eclipse and the coming April 8, 2024 total solar eclipse! Also, the point of longest eclipse for 2017 is just southeast of Carbondale at the geographic location of 37° 34' 4.3" North latitude, 89° 06' 10.0" West longitude. Just don't forget to drive east or west if clouds threaten to eclipse totality!

Hopkinsville, Kentucky
Duration of totality is 2 m 41.2 sec
Totality begins at 1:24 p.m. CDT

The civic boosters of Hopkinsville cite their fair city as the best spot in the nation for the eclipse. While Hopkinsville is a great location, you can travel for hundreds of miles east and west along the eclipse centerline and receive within 1 or 2 seconds of maximum eclipse duration. But if you would like to join a festive crowd, Hopkinsville will certainly be a great location to enjoy the eclipse.

Great Smoky Mountains Natl. Park
Duration of totality is 1 m 17 sec
Totality begins at 2:35 p.m. EDT

While this area is different from the rest by being closer to the northern limit line of total solar eclipse, this park will be an intriguing location to view the eclipse due to its expansive views. This site provides the possibility of seeing the Moon's shadow racing across the landscape, a dramatic sight that will add another dimension to your experience of the eclipse.

St. Joseph, Missouri
Duration of totality is 2 min 39 sec
Totality begins at 1:06 p.m. CDT

St. Joseph is right on the centerline of the eclipse path and enjoys one of the longest durations of any sizable city in the nation. A large eclipse viewing party is being organized at the Rosecrans Memorial Airport with educational speakers, solar telescopes, and more. If you would like to enjoy the eclipse in the company of astronomers, this is an ideal choice.

Nashville, Tennessee
Duration of totality is 1 min 57 sec
Totality begins at 1:27 p.m. CDT

Nashville deserves special note as the largest city wholly within the path of the total solar eclipse. While its location is offset from the centerline by about 20 miles, it still enjoys a good duration of nearly two minutes. Surely the nation's music capital will produce some memorable songs on the occasion of the Great American Eclipse.

Columbia, South Carolina
Duration of totality is 2 min 30 sec
Totality begins at 2:43 p.m. EDT

Columbia is a sizable city with long duration of totality and a fine network of highways for mobility on eclipse day. For millions of Americans along the Atlantic Seaboard, this will be the most accessible city with hotels in the path of total solar eclipse.

Science from solar eclipses

A total solar eclipse is a unique laboratory for learning about the Sun. Many scientific discoveries have been made during a total solar eclipse and new discoveries continue to be made.

The Sun's corona has been noted by observers in antiquity but a question in these early observers' minds was whether this was a phenomenon of the Moon, the Earth's atmosphere, or the Sun.

Astronomers obtained evidence that the corona is not associated with Earth's atmosphere during the 1860 total solar eclipse when photographs of the eclipse at widely separately locations showed the same features. By 1890, a pattern was found and a consensus was reached: the shape of the corona correlated with the 11-year sunspot cycle, therefore the corona had to be a solar feature.

The bright yellow line in this spectrum of the Sun is from helium. Astronomers found this element in the Sun's inner atmosphere decades before helium was identified on Earth.

During the 1868 total solar eclipse, astronomers used a spectroscope to identify a previously unknown emission line in the Sun's inner atmosphere. This had to be a spectral line emitted by a hot gas, but its nature remained unknown until 1895 when the same emission spectrum was identified on an earthly gas sample. This was the element helium, the fusion product of four hydrogen atoms, and the second most common element in the universe.

Albert Einstein in 1912 and Eddington's photographic plate from 1919 that measured star deflections.

The most famous result from solar eclipses is the supposed 1919 confirmation of Albert Einstein's general theory of relativity. British astronomer Arthur Eddington journeyed to the Atlantic island of Principe to photograph stars around the eclipsed Sun to test whether the Sun's gravity deflected them as predicted by Einstein's theory. The result was said to be positive and Einstein instantly became a global celebrity.

An aside: astronomers now know that Eddington's instruments could not possibly have made this sensitive measurement. Confirmation of Einstein's theory was premature.

In 1869, another spectral line was discovered which did not correspond to any known element. This was thought to be a new element provisionally named "coronium." It took nearly 70 years for this line to be identified as a heavily ionized form of iron called Fe^{13+}. These iron atoms have been stripped of 13 of their 26 electrons!

This identification of Fe^{13+} in the solar corona was remarkable because the only way that all these electrons could be stripped from a stable iron atom was if the corona was heated to several million degrees Fahrenheit.

This sets up the current major mystery in solar physics: spectral analysis clearly shows the temperature of the Sun's visible surface (the photosphere) to be nearly 10,000° Fahrenheit. So why is the corona so much hotter than the Sun's surface?

Solar physicists are debating two competing lines of thought to explain the coronal heating problem. Both involve the Sun's magnetic field. One involves waves in thin loops inside the magnetic field just outside the surface of the Sun. The other involves tiny solar flares, called nanoflares.

Several telescopes and a spectrometer on a common mount in Svalbard during the 2015 eclipse. Photo courtesy of the Solar Wind Sherpas.

International groups of solar physicists are traveling to solar eclipses around the world to try to solve this mystery. One group, the Solar Wind Sherpas, is led by Dr. Shadia Habbal. Another group is led by Dr. Jay Pasachoff.

Despite the availability of new solar spacecraft such as NASA's Solar Dynamic Observatory (SDO) which images in extreme ultraviolet wavelengths, ground-based observation of total solar eclipses in visible light still provides key information for solving the mystery of why the corona is so hot.

This background photograph shows the total solar eclipse of March 20, 2015 in the high Arctic archipelago of Svalbard. The exceptionally clear skies on that eclipse day yielded a bounty of scientific data that is still being analyzed to this day.

The corona of July 11, 2010 in white light as processed by Dr. Miloslav Druckmüller merged with an extreme ultraviolet image of the Sun by the SDO spacecraft. Composite image by Karen Teramura.

Historical solar eclipses across America

There is a long heritage of observing solar eclipses in the Americas. The accurate prediction of eclipses commenced in the 17th century and within a few decades had spread to the New World, as shown in this Mexican eclipse map of 1727.

The total solar eclipse of June 24, 1778 was the first to be carefully observed in the newly founded United States. David Rittenhouse, an American astronomer and mathematician, witnessed the eclipse from Philadelphia.

Thomas Jefferson, later the third American president, also tried to see this eclipse but was frustrated by clouds in Virginia. He wrote a letter to Rittenhouse remarking on the eclipse.

Two years later during the eclipse of October 27, 1780, an eclipse expedition was sent from Harvard University during the hostilities of the American Revolution.

Professor Williams of Harvard University led an expedition to Penobscot Bay in Maine and negotiated safe passage with the British forces occupying that area. Because of what is conjectured to be an error in his tables of the apparent motions of the Sun and Moon, Professor Williams narrowly missed totality.

On June 16, 1806, a total solar eclipse crossed North America from Baja California to Massachusetts. This was a long duration eclipse with nearly 5 minutes totality at the point of greatest eclipse. While the western United States was sparsely populated, this eclipse did pass over much of the American midwest and New England.

James Fenimore Cooper wrote a narrative of the eclipse, *The Eclipse,* describing townfolk's reaction in Cooperstown, New York.

The next eclipse widely observed in the young United States was the annular solar eclipse of February 12, 1831. This eclipse was instrumental in a slave uprising led by Nat Turner. He witnessed this eclipse and took it as a sign from God to begin an insurrection against slave holders.

The total solar eclipse of July 29, 1878 crossed western North America from Alaska to Louisiana. This eclipse involved the famous American inventor Thomas Edison, who accompanied an expedition to Rawlins, Wyoming, and attempted to make a temperature measurement of the corona. He was not successful because of interference from chickens!

The total solar eclipse of May 28, 1900 was widely viewed across the southeastern United States. The key scientific objectives of this era were spectroscopic studies of the corona and the continuing (but ultimately fruitless) search for a hypothesized planet inside Mercury's orbit, Vulcan.

The total solar eclipse of June 8, 1918 crossed the United States from Washington to Florida. This path is similar to the upcoming August 21, 2017 total solar eclipse and was the last time the path of totality crossed the nation from the Pacific to the Atlantic.

The total solar eclipse of January 24, 1925 was seen by millions of people in the New York metropolitan area and the northeastern United States.

A total solar eclipse crossed over the northwest United States and Canada on July 9, 1945 as the second World War was winding down. Newspapers of the day splashed eclipse news along with news of bombing raids on Japan.

The total solar eclipse of March 7, 1970 crossed the state of Florida and much of the Atlantic seaboard. Many of today's veteran eclipse chasers began their pursuit with this eclipse as it was accessible to many on the East Coast.

The last total solar eclipse within the contiguous 48 United States was on February 26, 1979 crossing a few states in the Northwest.

The total solar eclipse of July 11, 1991 was the last to touch any of the 50 United States. Many flew to Hawai'i for this eclipse and sadly most were disappointed by unseasonably cloudy weather on the Kona coast of the Big Island.

The partial phases of a solar eclipse is a great simulation of sunshine received by an outer planet of the solar system.

This map shows the calculated curves of dimmed sunshine levels (called *eclipse obscuration*). If you are along one of these curves, then at the moment of local greatest eclipse you will experience the simulated sunshine received by that planet (or dwarf planet).

Mars is 142 million miles from the Sun and receives about 43% of Earth's sunshine

Ceres is 257 million miles from the Sun and receives about 13% of Earth's sunshine

Jupiter is 483 million miles from the Sun and receives about 3.7% of Earth's sunshine

Saturn is 890 million miles from the Sun and receives about 1% of Earth's sunshine

Uranus is 1.78 billion miles from the Sun and receives about 0.27% of Earth's sunshine

Neptune is 2.79 billion miles from the Sun and receives about 0.11% of Earth's sunshine

Pluto is 3.67 billion miles from the Sun and receives about 0.06% of Earth's sunshine

Prince Rupert

Edmonton

Calgary

Vancouver
Victoria
Seattle

Portland
Helena

Sunshine on Saturn   Sunshine on Saturn
Sunshine on Saturn   Sunshine at Ura
Boise
Sunshine on Jupiter
Salt Lake City
Sacramento   Sunshine on Ceres
San Francisco

Las Vegas

Los Angeles

San Diego   Phoenix

Sunshine on Mars

Chihua

Portland, OR
Lake Oswego   Oak Grove
Johnson City
Maryhurst
Tualatin   Gladstone
West Linn
Oregon City
Uranus
Wilsonville
Neptune
Pluto   Beavercreek
Canby
Barlow
Total eclipse

Kansas City, MO
Kansas City
Kansas City
Total eclipse
Lake Quivira   Westwood
Pluto
Shawnee   Neptune
Overland Park   Prairie Village
Lenexa   Uranus
Leawood

St. Louis, MO
Castle Point   Uranu
Riverview
Granite City
Neptune
University City   Pluto   Brooklyn
Madison
St Louis   East St Louis   Fairmont Wash
Total eclipse   Alorton
Cahokia   Montreal

16

How dim is sunshine on the outer planets?

SIMULATING SUNSHINE ON OUTER PLANETS DURING THE TOTAL SOLAR ECLIPSE OF AUGUST 21, 2017

Saskatoon

Regina

Winnipeg

Thunder Bay

Bismarck

Sunshine on Mars

Québec

Montréal
Ottawa

Minneapolis

Pierre

Sunshine on Ceres

Milwaukee

Toronto
Buffalo

Boston

Detroit

New York

Chicago

Cleveland

Philadelphia

Omaha

Des Moines

Pittsburgh

Washington, D.C.

ne

Sunshine on Uranus

Cincinnati

Sunshine on Neptune

Denver

Sunshine on Jupiter

St. Louis

Norfolk

Kansas City

Path of the total solar eclipse

Raleigh

Sunshine on Neptune

ta Fe

Oklahoma City

Nashville

Memphis

Atlanta

Dallas

Jackson

New Orleans

San Antonio

Houston

Tampa

Miami

Nassau

Knoxville, TN

Uranus

Neptune

Pluto

Total eclipse

Augusta, GA

Total eclipse

Pluto

Neptune

Uranus

Charleston, SC

Total eclipse

Pluto

Neptune

Uranus

17

Why is this eclipse called the Great American Eclipse? Two reasons:

1. It cleanly bisects the nation and nearly everyone in the contiguous United States can reach the path of totality within one day's drive.

2. This total solar eclipse visits exactly one nation, the United States of America. Further, this is the first total solar eclipse to exclusively visit the USA since the country's founding in 1776!

From beginning to end, the partial stage of solar eclipse on Earth lasts 5 hours and 17 minutes.

The entire total stage of the solar eclipse lasts 3 hours and 14 minutes from the point where the shadow of the Moon first touches down northwest of Hawaii to where the Moon's shadow lifts off Earth at a spot in the eastern Atlantic Ocean south of the Cape Verde islands.

The total solar eclipse first reaches the United States at 10:15 a.m. PDT at Yaquina Head, Oregon.

The total solar eclipse last touches the United States at 3:50 p.m. EDT at Cape Romain, South Carolina.

This map gives an overview of the eclipse. An interesting fact is that the partial phase of the solar eclipse reaches five continents; North and South America, Asia, Europe and Africa!

In the 35 years from **1981 to 2016**, there have been **ZERO** total solar eclipses over the contiguous United States

Eclipse drought

In the 35 years from **2017 to 2052**, there will be **FIVE** total solar eclipses over the contiguous United States

August 23, 2044
August 21, 2017
August 12, 2045
April 8, 2024
March 30, 2052

Eclipse deluge

The total solar eclipse visits 12 states; Oregon, Idaho, Wyoming, Nebraska, Kansas, Missouri, Illinois, Kentucky, Tennessee, North Carolina, Georgia, and South Carolina.

Actually, tiny corners of two additional states, Montana and Iowa, are at the very edge of the path of totality, so a total of 14 states are in fact visited by the Moon's shadow.

At its widest point in southern Illinois, the path of totality is 71 miles wide.

When the total solar eclipse first reaches the coast of Oregon, it is traveling at a speed of about 2,400 miles per hour! This is faster than the world's speed record for a jet, the SR-71 Blackbird which had a top speed of 2,139 miles per hour.

The eclipse slows down as it reaches the point of greatest eclipse to "merely" a speed of 1,447 miles per hour, just under the top speed of a F-15 fighter jet.

Where is the very longest duration of the total solar eclipse? Xavier Jubier and Michael Zeiler have calculated this point to be at 37° 34' 04.3" North latitude and 89° 06' 10.0" West longitude with a duration of 2 minutes 41.6 seconds. This point is in the vicinity of Carbondale, Illinois.

Before you make plans to target this spot, understand that you can be along the center line of eclipse within a range of 42 miles and enjoy a duration within a 1/100th of a second below maximum duration.

You can also be within a range of 413 miles along the line of longest duration and enjoy over two minutes, 41 seconds (within 0.661 seconds of maximum). This span touches the states of Missouri, Illinois, Kentucky, and Tennessee.

So for quite a long stretch, you can be within an eye blink's worth of time difference to the theoretical longest eclipse time!

Totality across America

85%

90%

95%

2 min 50 sec

2 minutes

95%

90%

Eureka
85%

80%

75% San Francisco

San Jose
Santa Cruz
70%

65%

60% Santa Barbara
Los Angeles
Long Beach

55%

San Diego
Tijuana

50%

45%

40%

35%

30%

25%

Local maximum
eclipse is at
10:15 a.m. PDT
17:15 UT

Vancouver
Victoria

Jasper

Prince Albert

North Battleford

Red Deer

Lake Louise
Banff

Calgary

Kelowna

Saskatoon

Regina

Lethbridge

Medicine Hat

Vancouver

Bellingham

Aberdeen

Bremerton

Everett

Seattle

Tacoma

Wenatchee

Spokane

Coeur d'Alene

Kalispell

Havre

Glasgow

Minot

Williston

Dickinson

Bismarck

Astoria

Olympia

Yakima

Richland

Missoula

Great Falls

Portland

10:20 a.m. PDT
17:20 UT

Walla Walla

Lewiston

Helena

Bozeman

Billings

Miles City

Salem

Albany

Corvallis

Pendleton

10:25 a.m. PDT
17:25 UT

Butte

Salmon

Eugene

Bend

John Day

11:30 a.m. MDT
17:30 UT

Coos Bay

2 min 10 sec

Roseburg

Grants Pass

Medford

Crescent City

Klamath Falls

Mt. Shasta

Redding

Boise

Haley

Idaho Falls

Pocatello

11:35 a.m. MDT
17:35 UT

Cody

Yellowstone
National Park

Grand Teton
National Park

Jackson

Thermopolis

Riverton

11:40 a.m. MDT
17:40 UT

2 min 20 sec

Rapid City

Pierre

Twin Falls

Montpelier

Logan

Casper

Douglas

Gillette

11:45 a.m. MDT
17:45 UT

Chadron

Scottsbluff

11:50 a.m. MDT
17:50 UT

12:55 p.m. CDT
17:55 UT

Chico

Ukiah

Winnemucca

Elko

Green River

Rawlins

2 min 30 sec

Laramie

Cheyenne

North Platte

Yuba City

Reno

Carson City

Ely

Salt Lake City

Vernal

Craig

Fort Collins

Sidney

McCook

Santa Rosa

Sacramento

Provo

Boulder

Oakland

Modesto

Merced

Bishop

Price

Grand Junction

Moab

Montrose

Gunnison

Denver

Colorado Springs

Salinas

Fresno

Monterey

San Luis Obispo

Bakersfield

Las Vegas

Cedar City

St. George

Kanab

Monticello

Durango

Pueblo

Lamar

Dodge C

Boulder City

Grand Canyon

Trinidad

Raton

Lancaster

Barstow

Pasadena

Flagstaff

Winslow

Gallup

Los Alamos

Santa Fe

Kingman

Prescott

Albuquerque

Tucumcari

Amarillo

San Bernardino

Irvine

Palm Springs

Scottsdale

Socorro

Clovis

Oceanside

Phoenix

Roswell

Lubbock

Ensenada

Mexicali

Yuma

Gila Bend

Alamogordo

Hobbs

Abilene

San Felipe

Tucson

Willcox

Las Cruces

Carlsbad

Nogales

Douglas

El Paso

Ciudad Juárez

Pecos

Odessa

San Angelo

San Quintín

Hermosillo

Ojinaga

Del Río

Guerrero Negro

Chihuahua

Piedras Negras

Eagle Pass

Guaymas

Santa Rosalía

Nuevo Laredo

Laredo

Monclova

Los Mochis

Torreón

Monterr

Culiacán

La Paz

Durango

Mazatlán

Cabo San Lucas

20

Path of totality • Oregon

These maps are your guide to finding your optimum location on eclipse day. To see the full spectacle you must be within the path of totality, between 60 and 70 miles wide. For the longest duration, position yourself near the middle of the path of totality.

Aberdeen

Beaver

1-minute — Pacific City

1-min-30-sec — Neskowin

Sherida

1-min-40-sec

1-min-50-sec — Lincoln City

D

1-min-55-sec

Lincoln Beach

1-min 55-sec · 1 min 56-sec · 1 min 57-sec · 1-min 58-sec · 1-min 59-sec — 2 minutes

Otter Rock

1-min-55-sec

1-min-50-sec — Newport

1-min-40-sec

1-min-30-sec — Seal Rock

1-minute — Tidewater

10:15 a.m. PDT
2,514 MPH

The oval shapes depict the area that experiences the total solar eclipse during that instant. This is the shadow of the Moon as it races across the United States from the Pacific Ocean to the Atlantic Ocean in 93 minutes. These maps show the position of the Moon's shadow every three minutes along with its speed in miles per hour. Only the very fastest jets can keep pace with the shadow's velocity.

The yellow-orange curves within the path show the duration of total solar eclipse along that line. You can estimate durations between the curves by interpolation.

Oregon Dunes National Recreation Area

Coos Bay

August 21, 2017

The maximum duration steadily increases as the eclipse moves eastwards until southern Illinois, where the longest eclipse of 2 minutes and 41.6 seconds occurs.

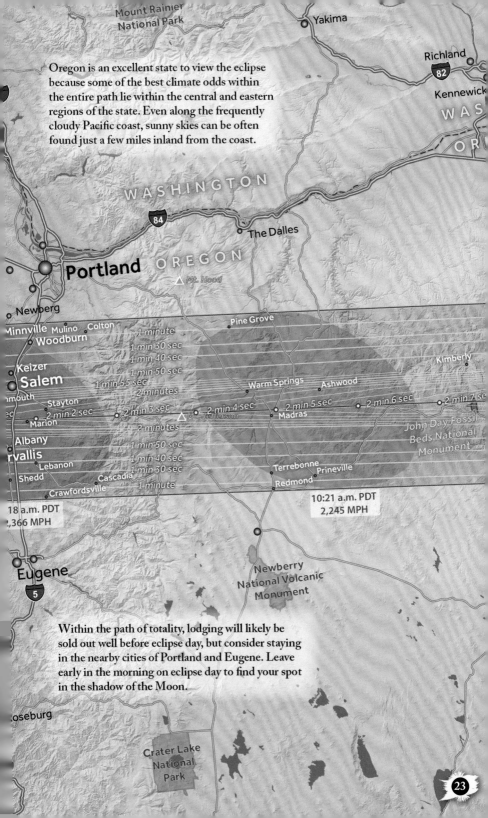

Oregon is an excellent state to view the eclipse because some of the best climate odds within the entire path lie within the central and eastern regions of the state. Even along the frequently cloudy Pacific coast, sunny skies can be often found just a few miles inland from the coast.

Mount Rainier National Park

Yakima

Richland

82

Kennewick

WASHINGTON

ORE

WASHINGTON

84

The Dalles

Portland

OREGON

△ Mt. Hood

Newberg

Minnville   Mulino   Colton   Pine Grove
        Woodburn
                            1 minute
                            1 min 30 sec
                            1 min 40 sec
Keizer   1 min 50 sec   Kimberly
Salem   1 min 55 sec   Warm Springs   Ashwood
mouth   2 minutes
        Stayton   2 min 5 sec   2 min 6 sec   2 min 7 se
    2 min 2 sec   2 min 3 sec   2 min 4 sec
    Marion   △ Jefferson   Madras
                    2 minutes   John Day Fossil
Albany   Beds National
rvallis   1 min 50 sec   Monument
    Lebanon   1 min 40 sec
Shedd   1 min 30 sec   Terrebonne   Prineville
    Cascadia   Redmond
    Crawfordsville   1 minute

18 a.m. PDT   10:21 a.m. PDT
,366 MPH   2,245 MPH

Eugene

5

Newberry National Volcanic Monument

Within the path of totality, lodging will likely be sold out well before eclipse day, but consider staying in the nearby cities of Portland and Eugene. Leave early in the morning on eclipse day to find your spot in the shadow of the Moon.

oseburg

Crater Lake National Park

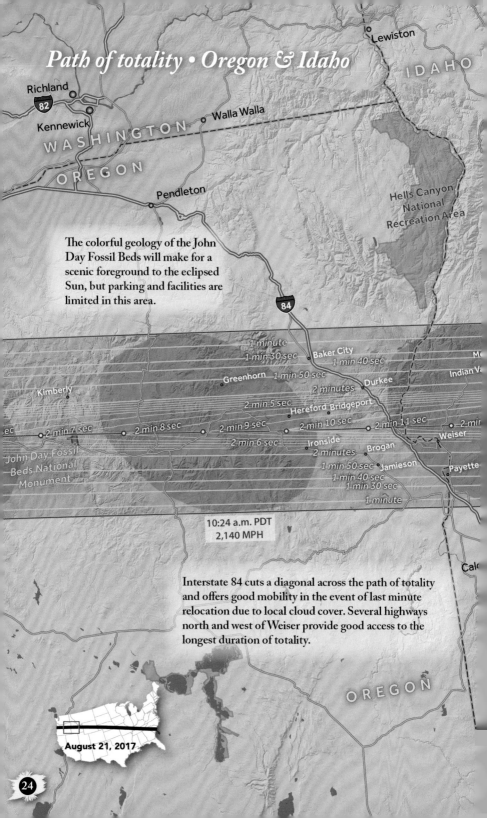

Path of totality • Oregon & Idaho

IDAHO

Lewiston

Richland

82

Kennewick

Walla Walla

WASHINGTON

OREGON

Pendleton

Hells Canyon National Recreation Area

The colorful geology of the John Day Fossil Beds will make for a scenic foreground to the eclipsed Sun, but parking and facilities are limited in this area.

84

1-minute

1-min 30-sec · Baker City

1-min 40 sec · Me

Greenhorn · 1-min 50 sec

2 minutes · Durkee · Indian Va

Kimberly

2 min 5 sec · Hereford · Bridgeport

2 min 7 sec · 2 min 8 sec · 2 min 9 sec · 2 min 10 sec · 2 min 11 sec · 2-mir

sec

2 min 6 sec · Weiser

John Day Fossil Beds National Monument

Ironside

2 minutes · Brogan

1 min 50 sec · Jamieson

Payette

1 min 40 sec

1 min 30 sec

1-minute

10:24 a.m. PDT
2,140 MPH

Cald

Interstate 84 cuts a diagonal across the path of totality and offers good mobility in the event of last minute relocation due to local cloud cover. Several highways north and west of Weiser provide good access to the longest duration of totality.

OREGON

August 21, 2017

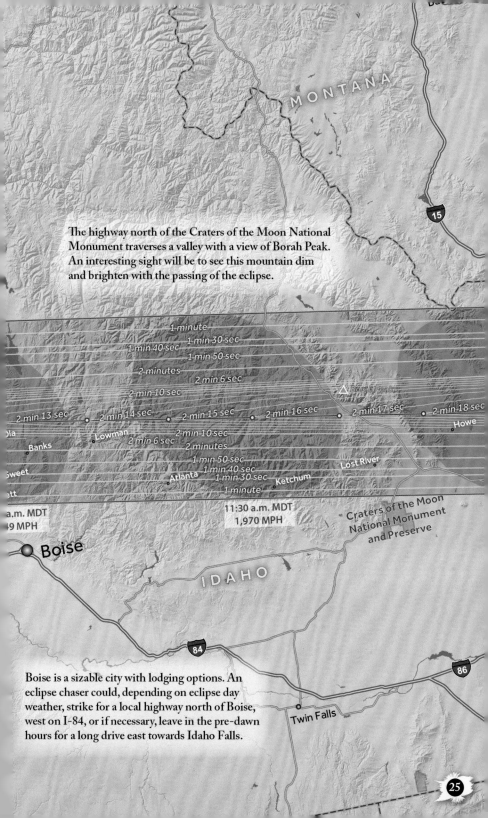

MONTANA

The highway north of the Craters of the Moon National Monument traverses a valley with a view of Borah Peak. An interesting sight will be to see this mountain dim and brighten with the passing of the eclipse.

1-minute
1 min 40 sec
1-min 30-sec
1-min 50-sec
2-minutes
2 min 6 sec
2 min 10 sec
△ Borah Peak

2 min 13 sec   2 min 14 sec   2 min 15 sec   2 min 16 sec   2 min 17 sec   2 min 18 sec
Ola   Howe
Banks   Lowman   2-min 10-sec
                             2-min 6-sec
Sweet   2-minutes
                    Atlanta   1-min 50-sec
                             1-min 40-sec
ett   1-min 30-sec   Ketchum   Lost River
                             1-minute

a.m. MDT   11:30 a.m. MDT   Craters of the Moon
9 MPH   1,970 MPH   National Monument
                                                              and Preserve

Boise

IDAHO

84

86

Boise is a sizable city with lodging options. An eclipse chaser could, depending on eclipse day weather, strike for a local highway north of Boise, west on I-84, or if necessary, leave in the pre-dawn hours for a long drive east towards Idaho Falls.

Twin Falls

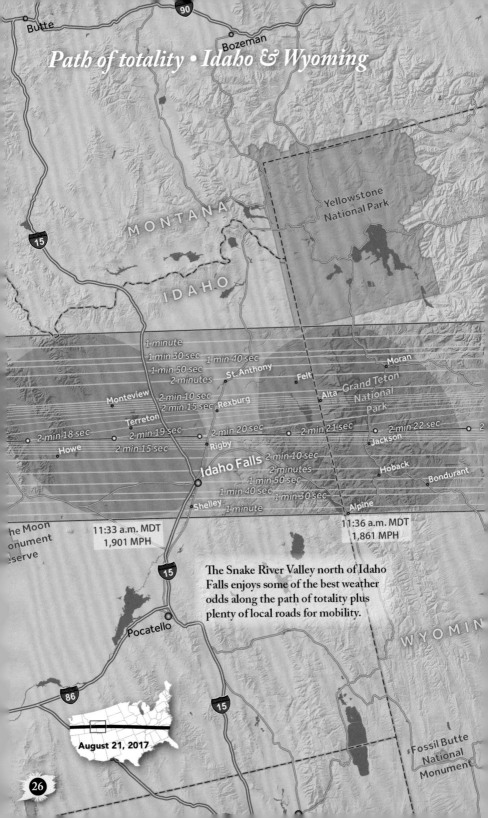

Path of totality • Idaho & Wyoming

Butte

90

Bozeman

15

MONTANA

Yellowstone
National Park

IDAHO

1-minute
1-min 30 sec   1-min 40 sec
1-min 50 sec
2-minutes   St. Anthony   Felt   Moran

Monteview   2-min 10 sec   Alta   Grand Teton
2-min 15 sec   Rexburg   National
Terreton   Park

2-min 18 sec   2-min 19 sec   2-min 20 sec   2-min 21 sec   2-min 22 sec
Howe   2-min 15 sec   Rigby   Jackson

Idaho Falls   2-min 10 sec   Hoback
2-minutes
1-min 50 sec   Bondurant
1-min 40 sec   1-min 30 sec
Shelley   Alpine
1-minute

he Moon   11:33 a.m. MDT   11:36 a.m. MDT
onument   1,901 MPH   1,861 MPH
eserve

The Snake River Valley north of Idaho
Falls enjoys some of the best weather
odds along the path of totality plus
plenty of local roads for mobility.

15

Pocatello   W Y O M I N

86

15

August 21, 2017

Fossil Butte
National
Monumen

26

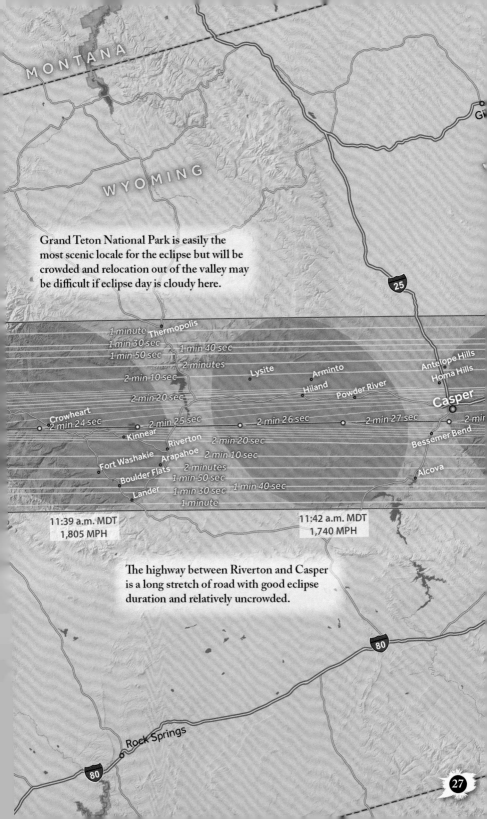

MONTANA

WYOMING

Grand Teton National Park is easily the most scenic locale for the eclipse but will be crowded and relocation out of the valley may be difficult if eclipse day is cloudy here.

1 minute   Thermopolis
1 min 30 sec
1 min 40 sec
1 min 50 sec
2 minutes
2 min 10 sec   Lysite   Arminto   Antelope Hills
                                    Hiland   Homa Hills
2 min 20 sec   Powder River
                                                        Casper
Crowheart
2 min 24 sec   2 min 25 sec   2 min 26 sec   2 min 27 sec   2 mir
        Kinnear   Bessemer Bend
            Riverton   2 min 20 sec
Fort Washakie   Arapahoe   2 min 10 sec
    Boulder Flats   2 minutes   Alcova
        Lander   1 min 50 sec
                1 min 30 sec   1 min 40 sec
                1 minute

11:39 a.m. MDT   11:42 a.m. MDT
1,805 MPH   1,740 MPH

I-25

Gi

The highway between Riverton and Casper is a long stretch of road with good eclipse duration and relatively uncrowded.

I-80

Rock Springs

I-80

27

Path of totality • Wyoming & Nebraska

Devils Tower National Monument

Rapid City

Gillette

WYOMING

Mount Rushmore National Memorial

Badla Nati P

Wind Cave National Park

SOUTH DAKOTA

Interstate 25 between Casper and the Glendo Reservoir provides quick access to good viewing locations. However, do not stop on the freeway to avoid being a road hazard.

NEBRASKA

1 minute

1 min 40 sec · 1 min 30 sec

1 min 50 sec

2 minutes

Antelope Hills

Homa Hills

Shawnee

2 min 10 sec

Mars

Douglas

2 min 20 sec

Casper

25

Glendo Reservoir

Agate Fossil Beds National Monumen

sec

2 min 28 sec

2 min 29 sec

2 min 30 sec

2 min 31 sec

Bessemer Bend

Esterbrook

2 min 26 sec

2 min 20 sec

Scotts-Bl

Alcova

2 min 10 sec

2 minutes

Torrington

National Mo

1 min 50 sec

1 min 40 sec

Veteran Huntley

Scott

1 min 30 sec

Wheatland

1 minute

**11:45 a.m. MDT
1,697 MPH**

**11:48 a.m. MDT
1,659 MPH**

People staying in Cheyenne or even the Denver area can leave early on eclipse day and access a good location through Interstate 25.

80

Laramie

Cheyenne

WYOMING

80

August 21, 2017

25

Fort Collins

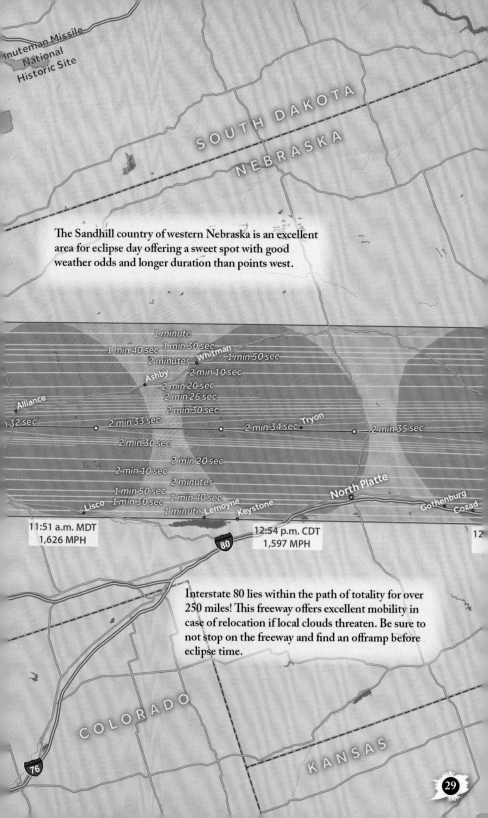

Minuteman Missile National Historic Site

SOUTH DAKOTA

NEBRASKA

The Sandhill country of western Nebraska is an excellent area for eclipse day offering a sweet spot with good weather odds and longer duration than points west.

1 minute
1 min 40 sec   1 min 30 sec
2 minutes   Whitman   1 min 50 sec
Ashby   2 min 10 sec
2 min 20 sec
2 min 26 sec
Alliance   2 min 30 sec
1:32 sec   2 min 33 sec   2 min 34 sec   Tryon   2 min 35 sec
2 min 30 sec
2 min 20 sec
2 minutes
1 min 50 sec   North Platte
Lisco   1 min 30 sec   1 min 40 sec   Gothenburg
1 minute   Lemoyne   Keystone   Cozad

11:51 a.m. MDT
1,626 MPH

12:54 p.m. CDT
1,597 MPH

12

80

Interstate 80 lies within the path of totality for over 250 miles! This freeway offers excellent mobility in case of relocation if local clouds threaten. Be sure to not stop on the freeway and find an offramp before eclipse time.

COLORADO

KANSAS

76

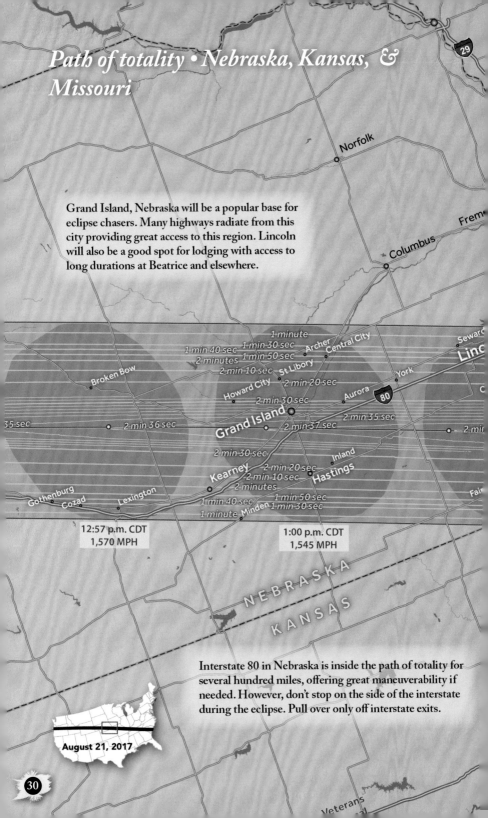

Grand Island, Nebraska will be a popular base for eclipse chasers. Many highways radiate from this city providing great access to this region. Lincoln will also be a good spot for lodging with access to long durations at Beatrice and elsewhere.

Norfolk

Columbus

Fremont

Seward

Linc

Broken Bow

1-minute
1 min 40 sec   1 min 30 sec   Archer   Central City
2 minutes   1 min 50 sec
2-min-10 sec   St Libory
Howard City   2 min 20 sec   Aurora   York
2 min 30 sec
35 sec   2 min 36 sec   Grand Island   2 min 37 sec   2 min 35 sec   2 mi
2 min 30 sec
Kearney   2-min-20 sec   Inland
2-min-10 sec   Hastings
2 minutes
Gothenburg   1 min 40 sec   1 min 50 sec
Cozad   Lexington   1-minute   Minden   1 min 30 sec   Fai

12:57 p.m. CDT
1,570 MPH

1:00 p.m. CDT
1,545 MPH

NEBRASKA

KANSAS

Interstate 80 in Nebraska is inside the path of totality for several hundred miles, offering great maneuverability if needed. However, don't stop on the side of the interstate during the eclipse. Pull over only off interstate exits.

August 21, 2017

Veterans

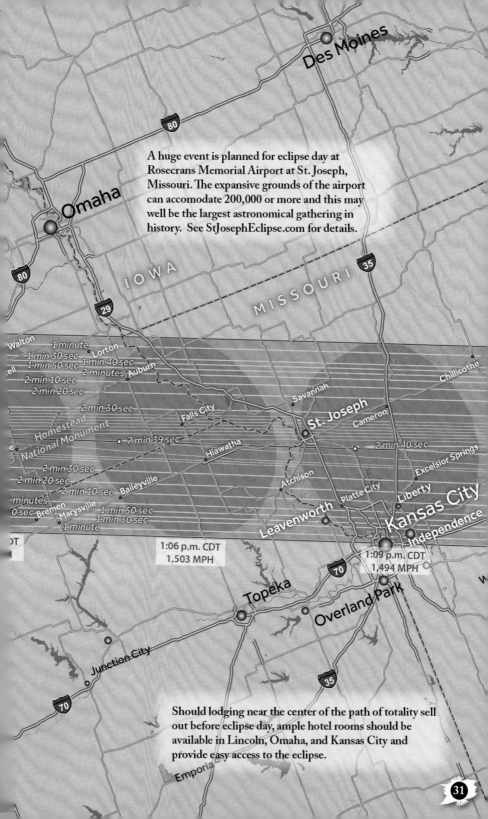

Des Moines

80

Omaha

A huge event is planned for eclipse day at Rosecrans Memorial Airport at St. Joseph, Missouri. The expansive grounds of the airport can accomodate 200,000 or more and this may well be the largest astronomical gathering in history. See StJosephEclipse.com for details.

IOWA

35

MISSOURI

29

Walton — 1-minute
1-min 30 sec — Lorton
1-min 50 sec — 1 min 40 sec
2-minutes — Auburn
2-min 10 sec
2-min 20 sec

Chillicothe

Savannah

2-min 30 sec

Falls City

St. Joseph

Cameron

Homestead
National Monument — 2 min 39 sec

Hiawatha

2 min 40 sec

2-min 30 sec

Excelsior Springs

2-min 20 sec

Atchison

Liberty

2-min 10 sec — Baileyville

minutes

Platte City

Kansas City

0 sec — Bremen — Marysville — 1-min 50 sec
1-min 30 sec

Leavenworth

Independence

1-minute

CDT

1:06 p.m. CDT
1,503 MPH

70

1:09 p.m. CDT
1,494 MPH

Topeka

Overland Park

Junction City

70

35

Should lodging near the center of the path of totality sell out before eclipse day, ample hotel rooms should be available in Lincoln, Omaha, and Kansas City and provide easy access to the eclipse.

Emporia

31

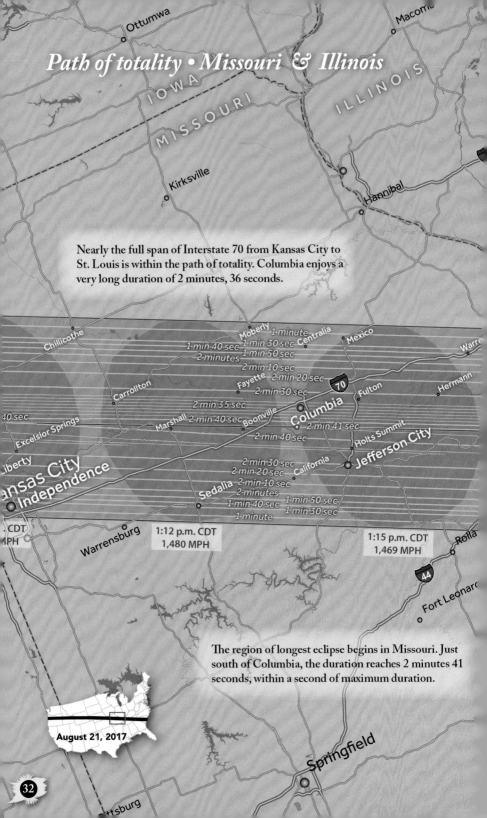

Ottumwa

Macom

IOWA

ILLINOIS

MISSOURI

Kirksville

Hannibal

Nearly the full span of Interstate 70 from Kansas City to
St. Louis is within the path of totality. Columbia enjoys a
very long duration of 2 minutes, 36 seconds.

Chillicothe

Moberly   1-minute

1-min 40 sec   1-min 30 sec   Centralia   Mexico

2-minutes   1-min 50 sec

Warre

2-min 10 sec

Fayette   2-min 20 sec

Carrollton

2-min 30 sec   Fulton

70

Hermann

2-min 35 sec

Marshall   2-min 40 sec   Boonville   Columbia

0 sec

2-min 41 sec

Excelsior Springs

2-min 40 sec

Holts Summit

Jefferson City

Liberty

nsas City

Independence

2-min 30 sec

2-min 20 sec   California

Sedalia   2-min 10 sec

1-min 40 sec   1-min 50 sec

1-minute   1-min 30 sec

CDT

PH

Warrensburg

**1:12 p.m. CDT
1,480 MPH**

**1:15 p.m. CDT
1,469 MPH**

Rolla

44

Fort Leonard

The region of longest eclipse begins in Missouri. Just
south of Columbia, the duration reaches 2 minutes 41
seconds, within a second of maximum duration.

August 21, 2017

Springfield

tsburg

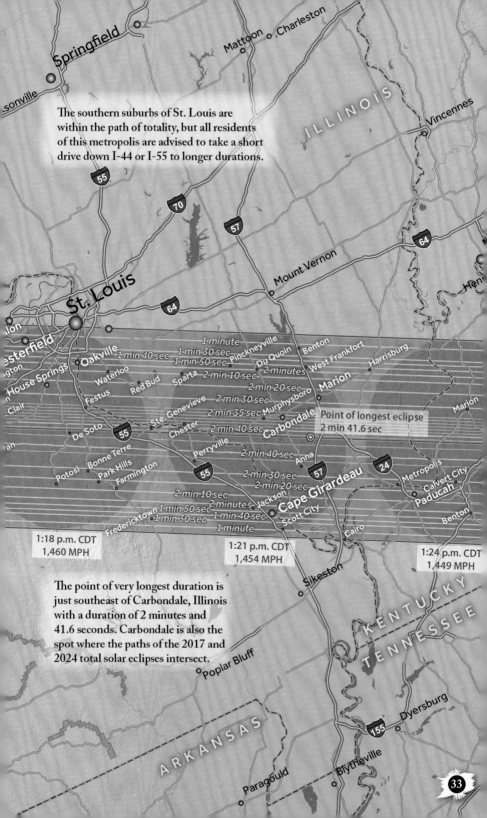

The southern suburbs of St. Louis are within the path of totality, but all residents of this metropolis are advised to take a short drive down I-44 or I-55 to longer durations.

ILLINOIS

Springfield
Mattoon
Charleston
sonville
Vincennes
Mount Vernon
Hen

St. Louis
esterfield
on
House Springs
Clair

1-minute
1-min 30 sec
1-min 40 sec
1-min 50 sec
Oakville
Waterloo
Red Bud
Sparta
Pinckneyville
Du Quoin
Benton
2-minutes
West Frankfort
Harrisburg
2-min-10-sec
Marion
2-min-20-sec
Festus
Murphysboro
Marion
2-min-30-sec
Ste. Genevieve
2-min-35-sec
Carbondale
De Soto
Chester
2-min-40-sec
Point of longest eclipse
2 min 41.6 sec
Potosi
Bonne Terre
Perryville
2-min-40-sec
Park Hills
Anna
Farmington
2-min-30-sec
57
Metropolis
2-min-20-sec
24
Calvert City
2 min 10 sec
Jackson
Cape Girardeau
Paducah
2-minutes
Fredericktown 1-min 50 sec
1-min 40 sec
Scott City
Benton
1-min 30 sec
1-minute
Cairo

1:18 p.m. CDT
1,460 MPH

1:21 p.m. CDT
1,454 MPH

1:24 p.m. CDT
1,449 MPH

Sikeston

The point of very longest duration is just southeast of Carbondale, Illinois with a duration of 2 minutes and 41.6 seconds. Carbondale is also the spot where the paths of the 2017 and 2024 total solar eclipses intersect.

Poplar Bluff

KENTUCKY

TENNESSEE

Dyersburg
155

ARKANSAS

Paragould
Blytheville

33

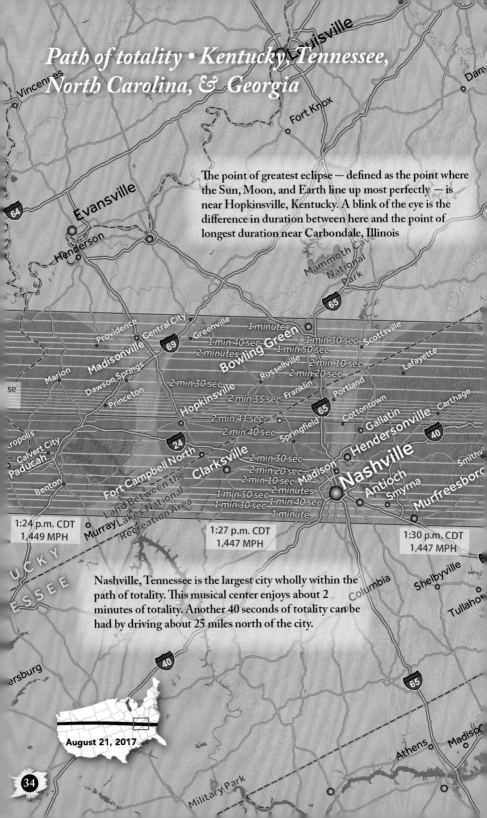

Path of totality • Kentucky, Tennessee, North Carolina, & Georgia

The point of greatest eclipse — defined as the point where the Sun, Moon, and Earth line up most perfectly — is near Hopkinsville, Kentucky. A blink of the eye is the difference in duration between here and the point of longest duration near Carbondale, Illinois

Nashville, Tennessee is the largest city wholly within the path of totality. This musical center enjoys about 2 minutes of totality. Another 40 seconds of totality can be had by driving about 25 miles north of the city.

1:24 p.m. CDT
1,449 MPH

1:27 p.m. CDT
1,447 MPH

1:30 p.m. CDT
1,447 MPH

August 21, 2017

Louisville
Vincenes
Fort Knox
Dan
Evansville
Henderson
Mammoth Cave National Park

65

Providence
Central City
Greenville
1-minute
Madisonville
1-min 40 sec
1-min 30 sec
Scottsville
2-minutes
Bowling Green
1-min 50 sec
Lafayette
Marion
Dawson Springs
Russellville
2-min 10 sec
2-min 20 sec
2-min-30 sec
Princeton
Hopkinsville
2-min 35 sec
Franklin
Portland
Carthage
ropolis
2-min 41 sec
Springfield
Cottontown
Gallatin
Hendersonville
40
Calvert City
Paducah
2-min 40 sec
Madison
Smithv
Benton
Fort Campbell North
Clarksville
2-min 30 sec
Nashville
Antioch
Murfreesbor
2-min 20 sec
Smyrna
2-min 10 sec
Land Between the
2-minutes
Murray Lakes National
1-min 50 sec
1-min 40 sec
Recreation Area
1-min 30 sec
1-minute

UCKY
ESSEE

Columbia
Shelbyville
Tullaho

40

ersburg

65

Athens
Madis

34

Military Park

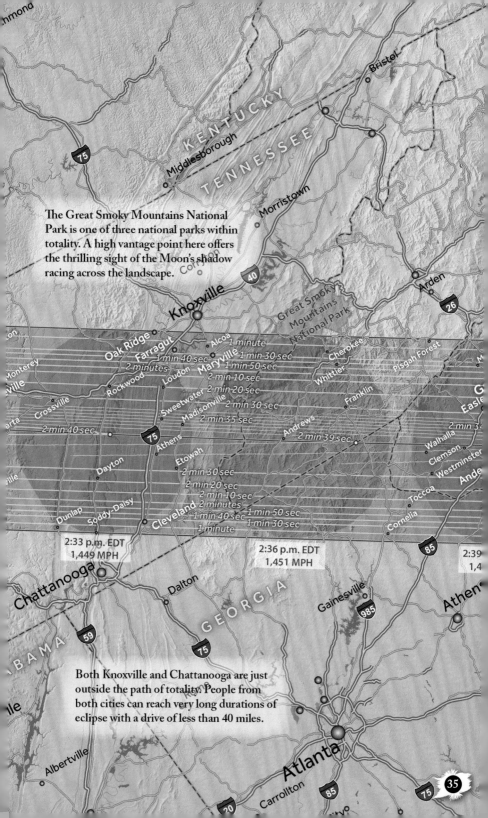

KENTUCKY

TENNESSEE

Richmond

Middlesborough

Bristol

Morristown

Arden

75

26

The Great Smoky Mountains National Park is one of three national parks within totality. A high vantage point here offers the thrilling sight of the Moon's shadow racing across the landscape.

40

Knoxville

Great Smoky Mountains National Park

Oak Ridge

Farragut

Alcoa

1 minute

Cherokee

Pisgah Forest

1 min 40 sec

Maryville

1 min 30 sec

Monterey

2 minutes

Loudon

1 min 50 sec

Whittier

Rockwood

2 min 10 sec

Franklin

Crossville

Sweetwater

2 min 20 sec

2 min 30 sec

Madisonville

Walhalla

Easle

G

2 min 40 sec

Athens

2 min 35 sec

Andrews

2 min 39 sec

2 min 3

Clemson

Westminster

75

Etowah

Dayton

2 min 30 sec

Ande

2 min 20 sec

2 min 10 sec

Toccoa

Dunlap

Soddy-Daisy

Cleveland

2 minutes

1 min 40 sec

1 min 50 sec

Cornelia

Andrews

1 minute

1 min 30 sec

85

2:33 p.m. EDT
1,449 MPH

2:36 p.m. EDT
1,451 MPH

2:39
1,4

Chattanooga

Dalton

GEORGIA

Gainesville

Athen

59

985

ALABAMA

75

Both Knoxville and Chattanooga are just outside the path of totality. People from both cities can reach very long durations of eclipse with a drive of less than 40 miles.

Albertville

Atlanta

85

75

Carrollton

20

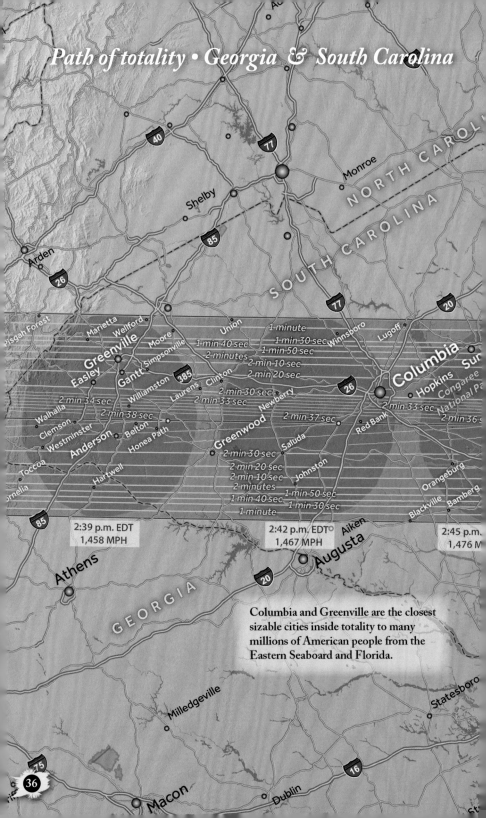

Path of totality • Georgia & South Carolina

NORTH CAROLINA

SOUTH CAROLINA

GEORGIA

Monroe

Shelby

Arden

Pisgah Forest

Marietta   Wellford

Greenville   Moore

Easley   Gantt   Simpsonville

Williamston   Clinton

Walhalla   Laurens

Clemson   Belton

Westminster   Honea Path

Anderson

Toccoa   Hartwell

Cornelia

Union   1-minute

1 min 40 sec   1 min 30 sec

2 minutes   1 min 50 sec

2 min 10 sec

2 min 20 sec

2 min 30 sec

2 min 33 sec

2 min 34 sec   Newberry

2 min 38 sec   Greenwood   Saluda   2 min 37 sec

2 min 30 sec

2 min 20 sec   Johnston

2 min 10 sec

2 minutes

1 min 40 sec   1 min 50 sec

1-minute   1 min 30 sec

Winnsboro   Lugoff

Columbia

Hopkins

Congaree

National Pa

Red Bank   2 min 33 sec   2 min 36 s

Orangeburg

Blackville   Bamberg

Sur

2:39 p.m. EDT
1,458 MPH

2:42 p.m. EDT
1,467 MPH

Aiken   2:45 p.m.
1,476 M

Athens

Augusta

Milledgeville

Statesboro

Macon   Dublin

Columbia and Greenville are the closest
sizable cities inside totality to many
millions of American people from the
Eastern Seaboard and Florida.

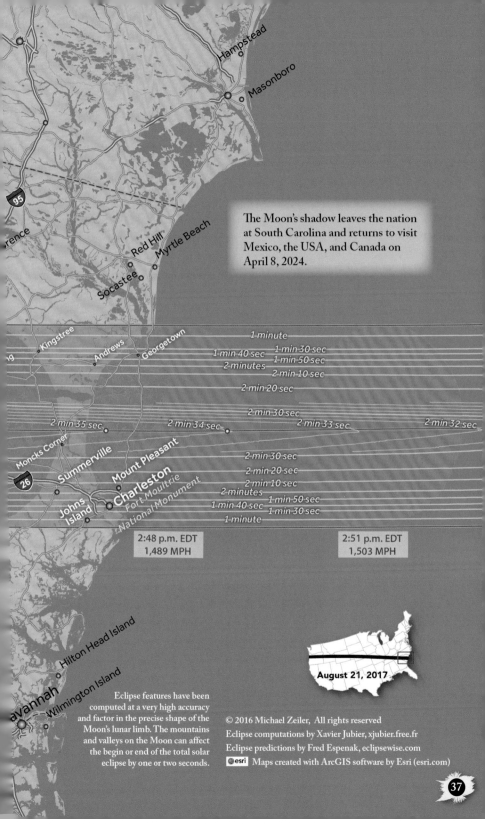

Hampstead

Masonboro

The Moon's shadow leaves the nation at South Carolina and returns to visit Mexico, the USA, and Canada on April 8, 2024.

Florence

Red Hill

Myrtle Beach

Socastee

Kingstree

Andrews

Georgetown

1-minute

1-min 40 sec

1-min-30 sec

1-min-50 sec

2-minutes

2-min-10 sec

2-min-20 sec

2-min-30 sec

2-min 35 sec

2 min 34 sec

2 min 33 sec

2 min 32 sec

Moncks Corner

Summerville

Mount Pleasant

2-min-30 sec

Charleston

2-min-20 sec

Fort Moultrie

2-min-10 sec

Johns Island

2-minutes

1-min-50 sec

National Monument

1-min 40 sec

1-min-30 sec

1-minute

2:48 p.m. EDT
1,489 MPH

2:51 p.m. EDT
1,503 MPH

Hilton Head Island

Savannah

Wilmington Island

August 21, 2017

Eclipse features have been computed at a very high accuracy and factor in the precise shape of the Moon's lunar limb. The mountains and valleys on the Moon can affect the begin or end of the total solar eclipse by one or two seconds.

Eclipse computations by Xavier Jubier, xjubier.free.fr

Eclipse predictions by Fred Espenak, eclipsewise.com

esri Maps created with ArcGIS software by Esri (esri.com)

37

North American eclipses past and future

These are the total solar eclipses that your parents or grandparents might have seen as well as those that you, your children, and grandchildren may see.

The last total solar eclipse on USA territory was over Hawaii on July 11, 1991. The last total solar eclipse in the contiguous United States was on February 26, 1979 in the northwestern states. The last coast-to-coast total solar eclipse across the USA was on June 8, 1918.

The next return of the Moon's shadow after 2017 will be on April 8, 2024 from Mexico, across Texas and the Midwestern states, and to the Canadian maritime provinces.

During the 21st century, a total of ten total solar eclipses visit the USA in 2017, 2024, 2033, 2044, 2045, 2052, 2078, 2079, 2097, and 2099.

May you, your children, and your children's children see as many of these celestial spectaculars as possible!

All the total solar eclipses over North America in the 20th century

All the total solar eclipses over North America in the 21st century

May 11, 2097
March 30, 2033
August 1, 2008
September 23, 2090
August 23, 2044
September 14, 2099
April 8, 2024
May 1, 2079
August 21, 2017
May 11, 2078
August 12, 2045
March 30, 2052
September 23, 2071
December 6, 2067

Eclipse resources

Learn more about the August 21, 2017 total solar eclipse at **www.GreatAmericanEclipse.com**. There you'll find more detailed maps, eclipse viewing advice, quality eclipse merchandise, and state-by-state guidance on the best places to view the eclipse.

These are other reputable websites with information specific to the 2017 eclipse:

- **eclipseglasses2017.com** is the preferred provider of quality eclipse viewers and filters
- **eclipsewise.com** offers authoritative eclipse predictions and information
- **xjubier.free.fr/tse2017map** is an outstanding on line eclipse map of the 2017 eclipse
- **eclipse.aas.org** is the portal site of the American Astronomical Society for the eclipse
- **eclipse2017.org** provides comprehensive information on national and local eclipse viewing
- **eclipsophile.com** is the essential site for eclipse climatology and weather
- **eclipse-chasers.com** offers general content on solar eclipses
- **BeingInTheShadow.com** explores human reactions to totality and community planning
- **AmericanEclipseUSA.com** gives good explanations on eclipse phenomena
- **eclipse.info** is the International Astronomical Union portal to eclipse resources

More websites, books, articles, magazines, and other sources are listed at **astrosociety.org/eclipse**